BELIEVE IT!

Senior Authors
Carl B. Smith
Virginia A. Arnold

Linguistics Consultant
Ronald Wardhaugh

Macmillan Publishing Co., Inc.
New York

Collier Macmillan Publishers
London

This work is also published together with other works in a single volume under the title: *Magic Times,* copyright © 1983 Macmillan Publishing Co., Inc. Parts of this work were published in earlier editions of SERIES r.

Macmillan Publishing Co., Inc.
866 Third Avenue
New York, New York 10022
Collier Macmillan Canada, Inc.

Printed in the United States of America
ISBN 0-02-131990-1
9 8 7 6 5 4

ACKNOWLEDGMENTS

The publisher gratefully acknowledges permission to reprint the following copyrighted material:

"Carmen," adapted from *Carmen* by Bill Binzen. Text and photographs copyright © 1969 by Bill Binzen. Reprinted by permission of Coward, McCann and Geoghegan, Inc. and Curtis, Brown, Ltd.

"Clouds," adapted from *The Cloud Book* by Tomie de Paola. Copyright © 1975 by Tomie de Paola. Adaption used by permission of Holiday House, Inc. Illustrations used by permission of the author and the Kerlen Collection of the University of Minnesota.

"The Dragon in the Clock Box," adapted from *The Dragon in the Clock Box* by M. Jean Craig. Copyright © 1962 by M. Jean Craig. Published by Grosset & Dunlap, Inc.

"Henry's Pennies" adapted from *Henry's Pennies* by Louise Greep McNamara. Copyright © 1972 by Louise Greep McNamara. Used by permission of the publisher, Franklin Watts, Inc.

"I stand on the rock," (Cherokee Indian). Copyright © 1972 by Norman H. Russell. Used by permission of Norman H. Russell.

"The Little Brown Bear" adapted from *The Little Brown Bear* by Cheryl Pelavin. Copyright © 1972 by Cheryl Pelavin. Used by permission of G.P. Putnam's Sons.

"Lucky and the Giant," adapted from *Lucky and the Giant* by Benjamin Elkin. Copyright © 1962 by Childrens Press, Chicago. Used with permission.

"Rachel," from the book *Rachel* by Elizabeth Fanshawe. Copyright © 1977 by Elizabeth Fanshawe. Published by Bradbury Press, Inc., and The Bodley Head. Used by permission.

"The Story Grandmother Told," adapted from *The Story Grandmother Told* by Martha Alexander. Copyright © 1969 by Martha Alexander. Reprinted by permission of The Dial Press.

"Winifred," adapted from *Winifred* by Anita Abramovitz. Copyright © 1971 by Steck-Vaughn Company. Used by permission of the author.

Illustrations: Ray Cruz, pp. 4-7; Jan Palmer, pp. 10-15; Tom Ballenger, pp. 16-25; Bill Woods, pp. 28-43; Robert LoGrippo, pp. 44-45; Ron Becker, pp. 46-59; Loretta Lustig, pp. 62-73; Tomie de Paola, pp. 74-81; John Thompson, pp. 84-91; Pat Merrill, pp. 92-101; Robert Jackson, pp. 102-103; Philip Wende, pp. 116-133. **Photographs:** Bill Binzen, pp. 104-113.

Contents

BELIEVE IT

There are many things you can do. You may be good at doing some things. You may not be good at doing other things. To find out what you can do, you must do new things all the time. It is very important for you to believe that you can do things.

In "Believe It!" you will read about a little bear who believes in himself. You will read about a girl who likes to make things. As you read, see if you can find other people who believe in what they can do. Can you do some of the things they can do?

The Story Grandmother Told

Martha Alexander

Part One
Tell Me a Story

Lisa said, "Please. Please, Grandma, tell me a story, please."

"All right, Lisa," said her grandmother. "What story would you like?"

"I'd like the one about Ivan and Lisa. It's the one about the green humming cat," said Lisa. "You know that one, Grandma. It goes like this."

One day Lisa and Ivan were on their way to a shop. They were on their way to get some ice cream. Then they saw a little man selling balloons. "Oh, let's get a balloon, Ivan," said Lisa. "We won't get ice cream this time."

"Mister, we want a balloon," said Lisa to the man. "Here is our money."

"Well, now, little girl," said the balloon man. "What balloon do you want? You can have one that hums. Just give me the money for the hummer."

Lisa and Ivan wanted a bright green balloon. They wanted a hummer, too. So they gave the man some more money for the hummer.

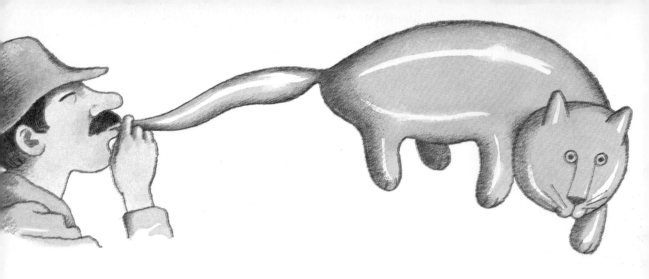

The little man put the hummer on the
balloon. He began to blow. He blew and
blew. He blew up a big green cat.
"Oh, mister, what a fine green cat!"
said Lisa.

The balloon man put a string on the cat.
He gave the string to Lisa. "Oh, thank
you, mister," said Lisa. "This is a fine
green cat!"

She took the string. The cat went up in
the air. It stayed behind Ivan and her.

Soon the green cat began to hum. Lisa
was very happy to have a humming green
cat balloon.

Part Two
The Green Humming Cat

Lisa and Ivan walked down the street.
They saw Lisa's friend, Annabelle. "What
a fine green humming cat you have," said
Annabelle.

"Oh, thanks," said Lisa proudly.

Then they saw Mrs. Goodman. She said,
"What a fine green humming cat you have."

"Oh, thank you, Mrs. Goodman,"
said Lisa proudly.

Joe and Mr. James liked it, too.
They thought it was the finest
green humming cat
they had ever seen.

HUMMMM HUMMM
HUMMMMM

Lisa ran home as fast as she could. She
wanted to show her mother the fine green
humming cat. Then —

BANG! The fine green humming cat was
gone! Only little bits of green balloon
lay all over the ground.

"Oh, Ivan, our new green humming cat
friend broke! But that's all right, Ivan. You
still have me."

14

"That's the story I want you to tell,
Grandma. And here comes Ivan. He wants
to hear it, too!"

"All right, Lisa," said her grandmother.
"That's the story I'll tell."

And that's the story Grandmother told!

THE LITTLE BROWN BEAR

Cheryl Pelavin

Part One
A Not So Special Bear

At one time there was
a little brown bear who lived
in the woods with other bears.
The little brown bear thought
that he was very special. But one day
he saw that one little brown bear
looked just like another one.
It made him sad that he was
no more special than any
other bear.

From his cave, he watched a deer.
He saw the deer eating leaves off the
trees. He decided he wanted to be like
the deer. He would eat leaves off the
trees. That would be really special.

The little brown bear found
some branches. He went to his cave.
He put the branches on his head.
He made sure they couldn't fall off.
Then he worked at looking quiet
like a deer.

Then he went out to show his friends
what a special deer he was.
But the other bears just asked him
why he had branches on his head.

17

So he went back to his cave.
He took the branches off his head.
Then he decided to become
a very special horse. He would
become a horse that could fish.
He had seen a horse like this one time
at the lake.

This time he trotted a lot.
And he worked at looking like a horse.
He trotted out by the lake.
There he saw some horses and bears.
He was about to show them
how a horse could fish.
Then everyone laughed.
No one had ever seen
such a funny-looking,
silly little horse.

The little brown bear went back
to his cave. He decided
that being a horse wasn't
such a good idea. After all,
horses looked like each other, too.
Then the little brown bear
had another idea. He decided
to become a great bird
with wings. He wanted to fly
like a bird. That would be
really special.

He made some wings. He made
them out of branches and leaves.
Then he went off to a high place.
There he worked at flying.

At last he was ready. He wanted
to show his friends that he could fly.
It was a little scary, but he jumped.
All the bears on the ground looked up.
What kind of new giant bird was this?
Some bears got out of his way
so he would not fall on them.

The little brown bear did fall.
He landed on top of a big tree.
It had lots of birds in it.
All the brown bears laughed at him.
The little brown bear knew
he looked very silly. He thought
his friends would always laugh
at him. He thought his friends
would never want to see him again.

Part Two
A Special Bear After All

The next day, the other bears saw that
the little brown bear was gone.
They looked for him all day and all night.
But they could not find him. At last
they were so tired that they all
went to sleep.

When the bears got up, they had
a big surprise. They saw
a big, scary animal with big wings
and big ears. The animal had green leaves
all over it. And it had a long green tail.

"I am the Great Green Groasle,"
it yelled.

All the bears just looked
at this very funny animal. Then they
went off to talk about what to do.

When they came back, they were angry
at the Groasle. They thought
the Great Green Groasle ate
the little brown bear.

"He was a great friend to all of us,"
they said. "We loved him very much."

Then the Great Green Groasle
laughed. He began to take off
his Groasle things. He took off
his wings and his ears and
his long green tail. He took off
his green leaves. And there he was,
the little brown bear! He waited
for everyone to tell him how happy
they were to see him.

But everyone just yelled, "So it's you,
little brown bear!" And they all
went off. They were very angry with him.
Just his mother stayed. She told him
he was a very silly little brown bear.

23

But after two or three days no one
was angry with the little brown bear.
Now they knew he was really
very special. He had special ideas.
He loved to make up things.
He loved to pretend.

So the bears asked the little brown bear
to be the head of every bear party
and every bear play. It was his job
to make up things. It was his job
to pretend. The little brown bear
loved his new job. And all the bears
saw how good he was at it.

At last the little brown bear
knew how special he really was.

What Is on the Table?

A. Look at the table below. It shows the number of turtles and frogs that Rico found. It also shows where he found them.

ANIMALS RICO FOUND		
Place	**Turtles**	**Frogs**
By the road	5	6
In the lake	4	7

Read each question. Look at the table to find the answer. Then write the answer on your paper.

1. How many frogs did Rico find in the lake? __7__

2. How many frogs did Rico find by the road?

3. How many turtles were by the road?

4. How many turtles were in the lake?

B. Look at the table below. It shows the number of boys and girls that play after school. It also shows where they go to play.

PLAYING AFTER SCHOOL		
Place	**Boys**	**Girls**
At the playground	12	13
In the park	8	4

Read each question. Look at the table to find the answer. Then write the answer on your paper.

1. How many girls go to the playground after school?

2. How many boys go to the playground after school?

3. How many boys go to the park after school?

4. How many girls go to the park after school?

Lucky
and the Giant

Benjamin Elkin

Part One
Giant Land

One morning Lucky went to the river
to catch some fish. But when he got
there, he had a big surprise. The river
was gone! There was no water— just dry
rocks. Lucky ran home to tell his father.

"We cannot live without our river. We
need water," said Lucky's father. Then he
went out to see the dry bed of the river.
"I will walk along this river bed
and see where it takes me," he said
to himself. "I will see if I can find
our river."

And he walked along until he
was way up in the hills. And then
he saw where the water from the river
was. The giant who lived in the hills
had it. He had put the river water
in back of a wall to make a lake.

"Well!" said the giant when he
saw Father.
"You have come for your river.
But you cannot have it."

29

"But I know the Law of Giant Land,"
said Father.

If I can do a giant's task,
The giant will give me what I ask.

"And do you know the other part
of the Law?" asked the giant.

If the task you cannot do,
It is seven years of work for you!

"Do you still want to do the task?"

Father looked at the giant's shoes.
They were not put on right. And
they did not go together. "He does
not look so smart," thought Father.
"Not so smart at all!"

"I am sure I can
do your task," said Father.

So the giant put one big foot
on the hill. And he put his other
big foot on Father's land.
"Let's see you do this," he said.

"That I cannot do," said Father.
"You know I am not a giant."

"Then you have to work
for me for seven years,"
said the giant. "Work!"
And Father began to work.

31

When Father didn't come home,
Mother said to Lucky,
"Where is your Father?
I will go and see if I can find him."
Mother went out to the dry bed
of the river. "I will walk
along this river bed and see where it
takes me," she said to herself.

And she walked along until she was up
in the hills. And there she saw Father
at work.

"Well!" said the giant when he saw
Mother. "You have come for your man,
but you cannot have him."

"But I know the Law of Giant Land,"
said Mother.

If I can do a giant's task,
The giant will give me what I ask.

"And do you know the other part
of the Law?" asked the giant.

If the task you cannot do,
It is seven years of work for you!

"Do you still want to do the task?"

Mother looked at the giant. His hat
was too little, and his coat was too big.
"He does not look so smart,"
thought Mother. "Not so smart at all!"

"I am sure I can do your task," she said.

So the giant took a rock and cracked it in two. "Let's see you put one rock into two boxes at one time."

"I cannot put one rock into two boxes at one time," said Mother. "You know I am not a giant."

"Then you have to work for me for seven years," said the giant. "Work!" And Mother began to work for the giant.

34

Part Two
Lucky's Pocket

When Mother and Father didn't come
home, Lucky said, "I thought Father
and Mother would be home by now.
I will go and see if I can find them."
Lucky went out to the dry bed
of the river. "I will walk
along this river bed and see where
it takes me," he thought.

As he walked, he saw many things
that he wanted. So he put them
into his pocket. At last Lucky came
to the place way up in the hills where
the giant lived. There he saw
his mother and father hard at work.

"Well!" said the giant when he saw
Lucky. "You have come for your mother
and father. But you cannot have them."

"But I know the Law of Giant Land,"
said Lucky.

> *If I can do a giant's task,*
> *The giant will give me what I ask.*

"And do you know the other part
of the Law?" asked the giant.

> **If the task you cannot do,**
> **It is seven years of work for you!**

"Do you still want to do the task?"

Lucky looked at his father,
hard at work on the giant's land.
"Yes," he said. "I will see if I can do
your task."

So the giant put one very big foot
on the hill. And he put his other big foot
on Father's land. Then he laughed and said,
"Let's see you do this."

36

"Why," said Lucky, "that's not hard
to do. I have some of my father's land
with me." From his pocket, Lucky
took some earth that came
from his father's land. He put the earth
on the ground. Then he put one foot
on it. So now he had one foot
on the giant's land and the other foot
on his father's land. "Now, let
my father go," said Lucky.
"I have done your task."

So the giant let Father stop working.

Then Lucky saw his mother hard at work.
"I have come for my mother, too,"
he said.
"You have, have you?" yelled the giant.
"Then you have to do another task."
The giant took up a rock and cracked it
in two. "There," he said, "let's see
you put one rock into two boxes
at one time."

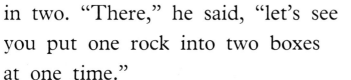

39

"Why," said Lucky, "that's not hard
to do. I have two boxes with me."
From his pocket, Lucky took
a very little rock and two boxes. One box
was smaller than the other. He put
the little rock into the smaller box. Then he
put the smaller box into the other box.
Now the rock was in two boxes
at one time. "Now, let my mother go,"
said Lucky. "I have done your task."

So the giant let Lucky's mother stop
working. There was one more thing Lucky
wanted from the giant. "We want
our river back, too," he said.

"Well then," said the giant.
"If you want your river back,
let's see you take all the water
out of my lake with a little spoon."

"Why," said Lucky, "that's not hard
to do. I have a little spoon with me."
From his pocket, Lucky took
a little spoon. And with it he began
to dig into the wall. Lucky dug and dug.
The water began to come out very slowly.
Then it came out very fast.
It didn't stop until all the river
was back in the river bed and the lake
was gone.

Lucky and his mother and father
looked at the giant. He looked so sad
that they were sorry for him. "Look,"
said Lucky to the giant. "There can be
water for everyone. Put a new wall
over here. Then you will have your lake.
And the water will still come down
to our land."

They all helped the giant make
a new wall. And by and by he had
a new lake. Then the giant
stopped looking sad. "You have been
so good to me," he said. "Let me know
if I can ever help you."

So Lucky and his mother and father
went home very happy. "Your father
and I are lucky," said Mother.
"We are lucky to have a boy as smart
and as good as you are!"

43

GIANT

One foot in the river,
  One foot in the lake—
What wonderful strides
  A giant can take!

The water goes "Squish"
  When he wiggles his toes.
Oh, giants have fun,
  As anyone knows.

His red rubber boots
  Reach up to his knee.
Why, puddles are nothing
  To giants like me!

—Elizabeth Sawyer

The Dragon in the Clock Box

Adapted from the story by M. Jean Craig

Part One
The Egg

One afternoon Joshua's mother went shopping.
She came back with a new clock. When she
took the clock out of its box, Joshua asked
her, "Can I have the box it came in?"

"Yes, Joshua, if you like. What are you
going to do with it?" asked his mother.

"Something," said Joshua.

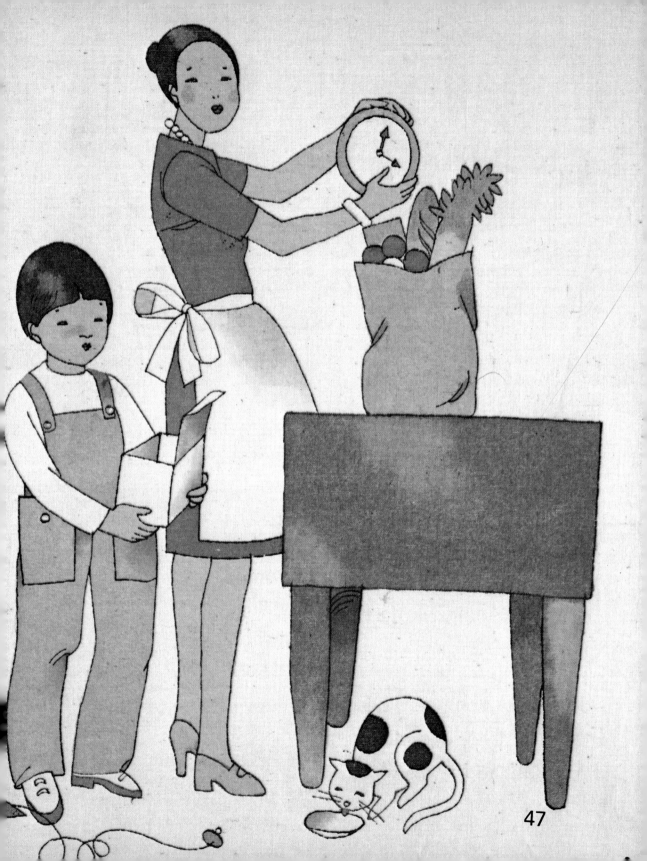

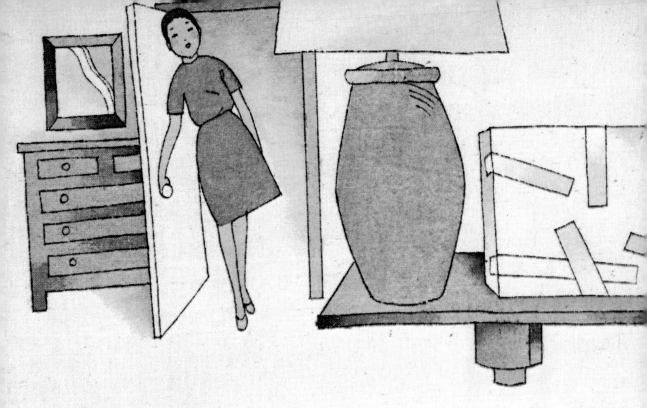

The next day Joshua's mother saw that he
had closed the clock box with a lot of tape.
She also saw that he had the closed box
with him all the time. He had it with him
when he was playing. He had it with him
when he was eating lunch. And that night
he put the closed box right next to his bed.

Joshua's mother came in to say good-night.

"Can you tell me what you have
in the clock box?" she asked.

"Yes, I can. It's a dragon's egg,"
said Joshua.

"Joshua—is it really?" asked his mother.

"Yes, it is, really," said Joshua, and he
went to sleep.

The next morning Joshua's father
asked him, "How is your dragon's egg doing
this morning, Joshua?"

"It isn't *doing*. It's just waiting," he said.

"What is it waiting for?" asked
Joshua's big sister.
"For it to be time," said Joshua.

"Time to hatch, you mean?"
asked Joshua's big sister, laughing.

"Yes, time to hatch," said Joshua,
without laughing at all.

"How did the egg get there in the clock box?"
asked his big sister.

"The mother dragon put it there," said Joshua.
"Before."

"Before? What do you mean, before?
Before what?" Joshua's sister asked.

"Before I closed the box with tape,"
said Joshua. And he took the clock box
out of the room.

Part Two
A Baby Dragon

Late that afternoon Joshua's father asked,
"How can air get into your box, Joshua?"

"The dragon doesn't need air yet,"
said Joshua. "It just needs to be quiet.
It needs to be quiet until it is hatched."

"When is it going to hatch?"
asked Joshua's sister.

"When it's ready to," Joshua told her.
"It will know when the time comes."

The next morning Joshua came down
to breakfast a little late. He put the clock box
next to his milk. There was a small hole
cut on one side of it.

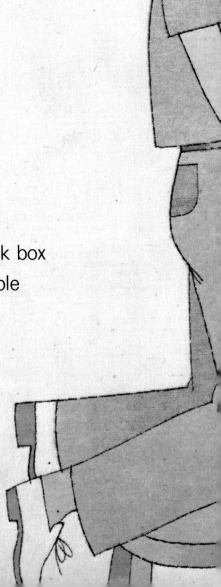

"He's a boy dragon," Joshua told everyone
as he sat down. "The egg hatched last night,
very, very late."

Joshua's mother asked slowly, "How could you
tell that the egg hatched? Did you hear it?"

"*He*, not *it*," said Joshua. "No, I didn't hear
him. He was very quiet. It was late
at night. It was time, and he was ready.
So I made a hole in the box just now.
He needs air."

"And now you can peek into the hole to see
what he's like," Joshua's sister said.

"I know what he's like," said Joshua. "He's
like a baby dragon. A baby dragon
just hatched."

"But you could look, just to be sure,
couldn't you?" asked his sister.

"I am sure," Joshua said. "And he isn't
ready for me to look yet. He wants to be
all alone because he is still very little."

The next day, Joshua's mother and father
and his big sister all had a lot of things
to do. No one said anything
about the clock box until it was time for bed.
Joshua's sister and mother came in to say
good-night. His sister asked, "Do you still
have a baby dragon in that box, Joshua?"

"Yes," said Joshua.

"Have you seen him yet?" his sister asked.

"Yes," said Joshua. "Now I have."

"Say, that's great! What does he look like?"
asked his sister again.

"He's green, and his wings are very soft.
They have tiny gold dots on them," Joshua
told her.

"How do you know that his wings are soft?"
his mother asked.

"It's always that way with baby dragons,"
said Joshua. "They always have soft wings
with tiny gold dots on them."

Part Three
Where Dragons Go

The next morning,
Joshua told his big sister, "The dragon's
name is Emmeline."

"Emmeline! But Joshua, that's a name for
a girl!" said his sister.

"I know, but he's a Chinese dragon. And
Chinese boy dragons like to have girls'
names. His eyes are red. And his wings
are getting strong," Joshua told her.

"Can I see him?" asked his sister.

"No," said Joshua. "He is still too little."

56

"But you look at him now, don't you?" asked his sister.

"He knows me now," said Joshua.

That night Joshua's father asked, "What are you going to feed the dragon, Joshua?"

"They don't eat when they are little," said Joshua. "Not baby dragons."

"Well, then, what are you going to feed him when he gets big?" his father asked again.

"I don't think I'll have to feed him then," Joshua said.

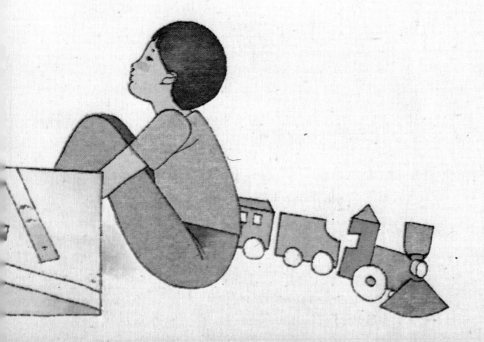

It was seven days after the day
Joshua's mother had come home
with the clock box. When Joshua came
down to breakfast that day, everyone said
"Good morning." But no one saw that
he didn't have the clock box with him.

That afternoon, Joshua's mother went up
to his room. She saw the clock box
by the window. The tape was cut off.
The box was wide open. She did not see
anything in the box.

"Joshua! Your box is open. Your dragon
is gone!" Joshua's mother called.

"I know," said Joshua. "He was ready
last night. And his wings were very strong.
He flew away."

"Did he really? But Joshua, where could he
fly to?" asked his mother.

"He flew to the place where dragons go,"
Joshua said.

Then Joshua walked over to the open box.
"I think this will be a very good box
for my crayons," he said. "I think I will
put my crayons in it right now."

And Joshua did.

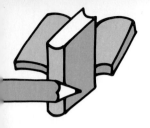

Mindy Gets a Surprise

Read the story about Mindy.

Mindy lived in a big city. She wanted a bike very much. But she didn't have the money to get one. Mr. Lucky's Bike Shop was on the street where Mindy lived. Every day Mindy went to Mr. Lucky's shop. She helped him with the bikes each time she came. Mr. Lucky and Mindy became good friends. One morning Mr. Lucky gave Mindy a present. It was a red bike with her name on it!

Read each question. Write the sentence that answers the question on your paper.

1. Where did Mindy live?
   Mindy lived in a big city.
   Mindy lived in the woods.
   1. Mindy lived in a big city.

2. What did Mindy want very much?

Mindy wanted a dog very much.

Mindy wanted a bike very much.

3. Why couldn't Mindy buy a bike?

Mindy didn't see a bike she liked.

Mindy didn't have the money to get a bike.

4. Why did Mindy go to Mr. Lucky's Bike Shop every day?

Mindy went to buy a new bike.

Mindy went to help Mr. Lucky with the bikes.

5. Did Mindy get a new bike?

No, Mindy did not get a bike.

Yes, Mindy got a bike.

Winifred

Part One
Signs

Winifred made things. She made things
to play with and things to look at.
She made all kinds of things.
She made big things and little things.
She made anything at all.

Winifred made so many things. But she
made them all so fast that they
came out looking funny. And sometimes
they didn't stay together long.

Winifred gave away all the things she
made. She gave them away
to the people on her street.
But no one knew what to do
with the things Winifred made.

Everyone said, "Thank you," but Winifred
was not happy. She knew that people
didn't really mean "Thank you."
They didn't know what to do
with Winifred's presents.

63

One day the woman next door said,
"Winifred, I know you like to make things.
Why don't you make signs?"

"Signs?" said Winifred.
"What a good idea!"

Winifred always went right to work
on a new idea. The next day she went
to the country with her family.
She saw all kinds of signs there.

When she got home, Winifred sat
right down and began to work.
She made signs just like the ones she
had seen in the country. But no one
could use the signs. No one
wanted them at all. So Winifred put
the signs up on the outside
of her house.

The next day, all kinds of people
stopped in to buy eggs or flowers.
They asked if they could buy dogs.
They asked if they could buy the house.
People came to the house all day long
because of the signs. They got mad
and yelled at Winifred because
things were not really for sale.
So Winifred took down all the signs.
She put them in the garbage can.

Winifred was not happy. But when
Winifred began to do something, she
couldn't stop. Every time she saw
a sign, she wanted to make one
just like it.

66

Part Two
More Signs

One day Winifred went to the zoo.
When she got home, she sat right down
to work. She made signs
just like the ones at the zoo.

But no one wanted the zoo signs.
So Winifred put the signs
up and down the street.
The street was something to see.
There were red and yellow signs
everywhere.

The next morning Winifred looked out
of her window. She had
a big surprise. Many people were
outside in the street. Police officers were
there, too. People were yelling
at each other. They had seen
the signs. They thought that the animals
had run away from the zoo.

Some people looked scared. Some people
looked mad. Then Winifred saw
the woman next door. She looked
more scared than anyone.
The police officers began to take down
Winifred's signs. They put them
in the police cars.

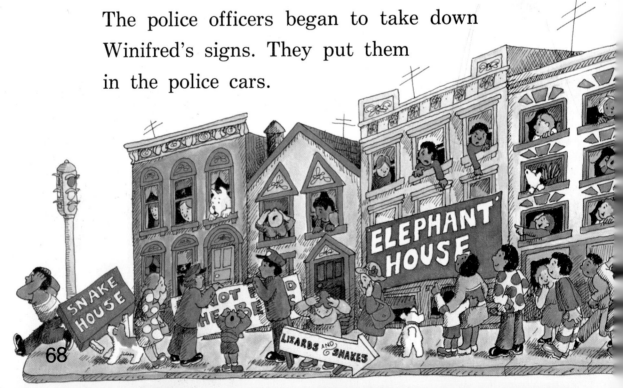

Winifred wanted to run. Winifred
wanted to hide. Winifred wanted
to fly away. But she didn't.
She called from her window, "Wait!
Wait! Wait!"

Winifred ran down to the street.
"I'm sorry. I'm really sorry, everyone!"
she called out. "I didn't mean
to scare anyone."

All the people in the street
stopped yelling at each other.
They all looked at Winifred.
Everyone was quiet.

Then the woman next door said,
"Things are going to be all right,
Winifred. You were a good girl
to tell everyone you made the signs.
Will you help me into my house?"

So Winifred helped the woman back
into her house. They sat and talked.
The other people walked slowly away.
The police officers drove away. They took
the last of Winifred's signs with them.

When Winifred went back to her house,
she had a new idea. She got out
her crayons and her paints.
She made a very, very big sign.

A friend helped Winifred put up
the sign over her doorway.

From then on, Winifred had a lot of work
to do. She got an order from Bob Cook
for his tree house.

Then she had to make a sign
for the people next door.

Next she made a sign for the new baby
down the street.

You never saw such great signs.

One day Winifred made a tiny sign
for the woman next door. She wanted it
for her cat. The sign had the cat's name
on it.

At last Winifred was happy. Now people
could use the things that she made.
When Winifred made a sign to order,
people said "Thank you, thank you."
And Winifred knew that they
really did mean it.

Clouds

Tomie de Paola

The next time you go outside,
look up at the sky.
You may see clouds.

Clouds are little drops of water or ice.
They are in the air high above the earth.
If you could jump on a bird and fly way up,
you would see clouds all over the earth.

There are many kinds of clouds.
Some are high up. Some are in the middle.
Some are low down in the sky.

The three main kinds of clouds are called
cirrus, cumulus, and *stratus* clouds.
You can tell them apart
by the way they look.
You can tell by where they are
in the sky, too.

Cirrus clouds are white and feathery.
They are the highest clouds.
They are sometimes called "mares' tails."

Cumulus clouds are puffy.
They look like cauliflowers.
They are flat at the bottom, too.
Cumulus clouds are always moving.
They are low down in the sky.

 This is a cloud. This is a cauliflower.

Stratus clouds are low, too.
They are wide and flat and gray.
They are sometimes called "high fogs."
Rain or snow may fall from stratus clouds.

Fog is a cloud made of water drops.
It is a cloud on the ground.
If you live on a high mountain,
you may see a lot of fog.
Fog can come right into your yard.

Long ago, people looked at the clouds
and saw things.
People saw giants, animals, ships,
and castles, too!

There are some sayings about clouds.
They help tell if it will rain or not.
Here are some sayings for travelers.

Evening red and morning gray,
Set the travelers on their way.

Evening gray and morning red,
Rain will fall upon your head.

So you see, there is much to know about clouds.

What Do You Hear?

A. Say these words.

found   la<u>st</u>

<u>foun**d**</u>

Look at the two letters at the end.
These letters spell the end sounds.
Now look at the words below. Choose
the letters that will make a word.
Write the word on your paper.

1. playgrou＿＿   nd   st
   1. playground
2. fa＿＿   nd   st
3. frie＿＿   nd   st
4. ju＿＿   nd   st
5. behi＿＿   nd   st
6. arou＿＿   nd   st
7. mu＿＿   nd   st
8. ha＿＿   nd   st
9. mo＿＿   nd   st
10. ki＿＿   nd   st

B. Say these words.

f̲l̲ew	b̲r̲anches
s̲w̲im	s̲c̲ales
s̲t̲ay	c̲l̲own

Look at the two letters at the front.
These letters spell the first sounds.
Now look at the words below. Choose
the letters that will make a word.
Write the word on your paper.

1. __ __owers   br   fl   st
2. __ __ock   sw   cl   br
3. __ __op   br   st   sc
4. __ __other   st   fl   br
5. __ __ory   cl   br   st
6. __ __eakfast   fl   sw   br
7. __ __im   cl   fl   sw
8. __ __are   br   sc   cl
9. __ __oud   cl   st   br
10. __ __ayed   st   cl   fl

Rachel

Elizabeth Fanshawe

Today I made a birthday card
for my mother.
My teacher helped me.
I am in a wheelchair.
I go to school with my sister.

We have to work hard, but it's fun.
It was my turn to feed the mice
this morning.

When it's time to go home, we all
help to clean up.

Sometimes my friends like to push me.
But I can do it alone, too. I go fast
down the ramp.

My mother gets us at school, because I
can't get on the bus.
My chair goes in the car.

Some days, Grandma comes to see me.
She always brings something for my dog.

We all help to get something to eat.
My father sits next to me at the table.

On Thursdays, we go to Brownies.
I like the games best.

I can almost swim without help now.
Someday soon, I am going to learn to
ride a horse, too.

Last year we went to the mountains.
Everyone laughed when they saw
the pictures I took.

My father and I talk about
what I will be when I grow up.
There are so many things I could be.

Where's the Dog?

Bernice Myers

Part One
The Cat

Willie found a cat
on the road
and took him home.

"No cats," said his father.

"Your father is right,"
said his mother.

"Please, can't he stay?"
asked Willie.
"Suzy and I
will take care of him.
Please, please? Yes?
We **can** keep him? Great!"

Suzy ran to the cat
with some milk.
When the milk was gone,
Suzy took the cat on her lap.

"Nice cat," she said.

"Now, let me hold the cat,"
said Willie.

"No!
It's still my turn,"
said Suzy.

"Let me have a turn
right now," said Willie.
"I'm the one who found
the cat!"
Willie took the cat
away from Suzy.

"Can I hold him now?"
asked Suzy.
"Are you going to give
him to me?"

"No! He is mine!"
yelled Willie.
"I found him.
Go get another pet
if you want one
so much."

Suzy ran to her room.
"I will!" she thought.
"I'll get a pet
that will be just mine."

Part Two
Howard

Suzy walked down
the road.
After a long time
she still had not found
a pet.
She sat down to think.

Soon, she was pulling
a rope with a loop
at the end of it.

When she got home,
she said to her mother,
"Watch out for Howard."

Suzy's mother
didn't see anything
but a rope with a loop
at the end of it.
"Howard? Who's Howard?"
she asked.

Then Willie came in
with his cat.
"Why are you pulling
that rope with a loop
at the end of it?"
he asked.

"Because there's a dog there,"
said Suzy.

"A dog?" said Willie.
"I don't see any dog."

"That's because
he's invisible
to everyone but me!"

"What does he look like then?"
asked Willie.

"He has big brown eyes
and a long tail," said Suzy.

"Well, why can't I
hear him bark?" asked Willie.

"Because his bark is invisible,
too," said Suzy.

Suzy got down on the ground
next to the loop.
"Howard!" she said.
"Don't lick me.
Stop, I say.
All right,
all right.
I'll take you out
for a walk."

Suzy ran out
pulling the rope.

Willie wanted to play
with his cat,
but the cat ran away.
From the window,
Willie could see Suzy
playing with Howard.
Suzy threw an old shoe.
Then she and Howard
ran after the shoe.
"Nice dog," Suzy yelled.

Suzy came back
into the house
pulling Howard's rope.
"Do you want my cat?"
Willie asked.
"I'll give you my cat
for your dog."

"For Howard? Never!"

"Please, Suzy?"
asked Willie again.

"All right,"
Suzy said at last.
"Here is the rope.
Where is the cat?"

"In the other room,"
said Willie.

Willie took the rope
and ran out to play
with Howard.

When he came back,
Suzy was playing
with the cat.
Willie just looked
at them.
Then he called to his dog,
"Stop it, Howard.
Leave the cat alone!"
Willie ran around
the room after Howard.

The cat ran out.

"You scared my cat,"
Suzy yelled at Willie.

"I did not!
The **dog** did!" said Willie.

"I didn't see
any **dog**," Suzy said.

"That's because
the dog is
invisible,"
said Willie.

Suzy and Willie
looked at each other
and began to laugh.

Then Suzy ran out
to get the cat.

"Here, Willie,
it's your turn
to hold **our** cat."

I stand on the rock.
Ho, bear!
Beware of me!

I stand on the tree.
Ho, eagle!
Beware of me!

I stand on the mountain.
Ho, enemy!
Beware of me!

I stand in the camp.
Ho, chiefs!
Beware of me!

Here comes a bee!
I run and hide!
He would sting me!

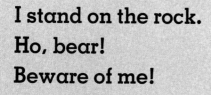

CARMEN

Bill Binzen

It was raining. It was always raining
in New York.

Carmen ran home from school.
She thought, "In Puerto Rico it rains
for a little, and then the sun comes out.
I wish it were like that here!"

Carmen had just moved to New York from Puerto Rico. She had moved with her family. She missed her home in Puerto Rico. She missed the sun. And she missed her friends, too.

On her way home, Carmen had to buy some potatoes for her mother. She had the money in her pocket.

After she got the potatoes, she came out to the side of the street. There was so much rain water running down the street. Carmen decided to jump over the water. But she couldn't make it, and she fell down right in the water! The potatoes flew all over the street, and Carmen got all wet.

Carmen was happy to get home.
She got out of her wet dress.
She decided to put on
her very nice dress. It would help
to make her happy. She thought
of the day when her mother gave her
the dress, back in Puerto Rico.

"I wish I had something to do,"
Carmen thought. "If only I had
a friend to play with." Her brother
was home, but he was playing
with his new car.

For a long time Carmen sat
in the window and looked down
on the street. She watched
a garbage truck come slowly by.

The garbage collectors walked
behind the truck. They put the garbage
in the back of the truck.

"I wouldn't want to be a garbage collector
in all this rain," Carmen said.

"You wouldn't want to be one
if the sun were out," said her brother.

Then another truck came down the street.

"I wouldn't want to drive a truck
in all this rain," Carmen thought.
But she didn't say it. She didn't want
her brother to hear.

There wasn't much to watch
from the window after that.
There was no one in the street.

Carmen was sad. "Why does it always
have to rain?" she thought. "I wish
there were something to do!" She was
feeling sorry for herself.

Just then Carmen saw something!
She saw a little girl with long hair.
She, too, was looking out a window.
She had on a dress very much
like Carmen's and she looked
about as old as Carmen.

Carmen put her hand up, and
the other girl put her hand up, too.
Then Carmen began to feel good
all over. She got her doll and put
it up in the window next to her.

The other girl smiled when she saw
the doll. Then she went away
for a little time. When she came back,
she had a little bear.

Soon the girls were making signs
to each other, and making up
all kinds of silly games.
Time flew by. They forgot
about the rain.

Then, the other girl pointed at Carmen.
Then she pointed down at the street.

"I wonder what she means," Carmen thought,
as the little girl pointed again.

Then Carmen saw that the rain
had stopped. Now she knew what
all that pointing was about. Her new friend
was saying, "I'll see you outside."

"Please, Mother, can I go out?"
Carmen asked. Her mother hardly had
time to say yes before Carmen was
out the door and running down
to the street.

Her friend was waiting!

For a little time the two girls
didn't know what to say.
It was funny being together,
face to face.

"Hello," said the girl. "I'm Liza."

"Hello," said Carmen. "I'm Carmen."

"Let's play a game," said Liza.

"Yes, let's," said Carmen.

They had so much fun together
playing games on the street.

Soon Carmen's mother called,
"Carmen, it's time for you to come
to eat."

"Who wants to eat?" thought Carmen.
But then she smiled and said,
"See you soon, Liza."

Liza smiled. "Yes, I'll see you
soon," she said.

When the next day came, it was raining
again. Rain, rain, rain. But Carmen
didn't care, and Liza didn't care.

This time, they were in one house together. And they were in one window together. And the doll and the bear were right there with them.

Can You Hear the Sound?

Say each picture name. The blue letters spell a long vowel sound. Listen to that sound when you say the words. Then read the story. Find the words with letters that spell the same long vowel sound. Write the words on your paper.

cake

train

A. Fred had to rake the leaves. But it began to rain. So Fred went in. What could he do? He could make a game. He could paint. He could just wait for the rain to stop, too.

1. rake

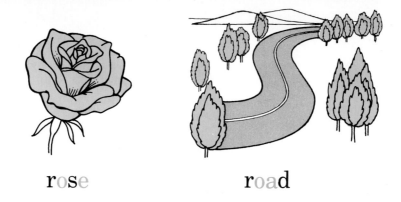

rose road

B. Tom's father went to see his boat. But it was not there. He put on his coat and walked all around the lake. When he found his boat, he took it back home. He tied up the boat with a rope.

queen beans

C. Kim peeked out of the window. She saw the big tree. It had lost its last leaf. The leaf had fallen in the street. Kim thought about how green the tree was in May.

Henry's Pennies

Louise Greep McNamara

Part One
A Lot of Pennies

Henry loved Sundays. Every Sunday,
at breakfast, Henry would give his father
a special look. And then his father
would put his hand in his pocket
as Henry watched.

"Let's see how many pennies I have
for you today," his father would say.

116

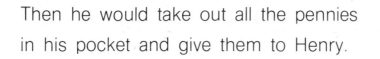

Then he would take out all the pennies
in his pocket and give them to Henry.

Henry had a lot of pennies. He loved to
count them. "One, two, three..." He would
never know just how many he had, so he
counted all of them every Sunday.

People sometimes asked him
what he was going to do with all his pennies.
All he ever said was, "You'll see."
But Henry didn't really know yet.

Sometimes he thought of all the candy
he could buy with his pennies. But then
he would think about the big boys.
What if they took his candy away from him?

And even if the boys didn't take
his candy, his mother would never
let him have it. She always said
too much candy wasn't good for you.
Even if he could find a way to hide
the candy in his room, his baby sister
would be sure to find it.

So Henry just said "You'll see," when
people asked about his pennies.

One day at school his friend Chippy said
to him, "Are you going to the fair?"

"What fair?" asked Henry.

"The fair in the school playground
on Friday," said Chippy. "It will be fun.
There will be candy and things to eat.
There will be pony rides and a lot
of old things that you can buy. I know
all about it. My mother is running
the White Elephant Sale."

"A white elephant sale? Zowee!"
said Henry. "Zowee!"

That night Henry asked his mother
if he could go to the fair.
When she said yes, he was so happy
he yelled "Zowee!" again.

When he went to bed, Henry didn't
fall asleep right away. He thought about
what he was going to do with his pennies.
On Friday he would buy a white elephant!

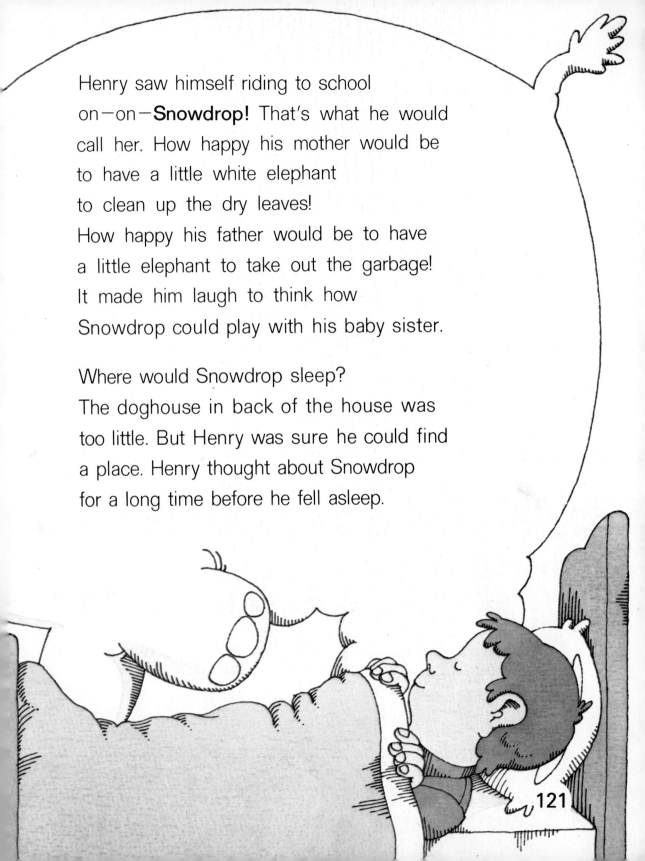

Henry saw himself riding to school
on—on—**Snowdrop!** That's what he would
call her. How happy his mother would be
to have a little white elephant
to clean up the dry leaves!
How happy his father would be to have
a little elephant to take out the garbage!
It made him laugh to think how
Snowdrop could play with his baby sister.

Where would Snowdrop sleep?
The doghouse in back of the house was
too little. But Henry was sure he could find
a place. Henry thought about Snowdrop
for a long time before he fell asleep.

121

Part Two
Pennies and Peanuts

The morning of the fair came at last.
Henry jumped out of bed fast.
After breakfast he ran to his room.
He put his pennies in his special sock.
He put the sock in his coat pocket
and ran off to school.

At school, everyone asked,
"What do you have in the sock, Henry?"
But he didn't want people to know.
He didn't let go of the sock all morning.

But Henry's friend Chippy could hear
the pennies in the sock. "Gee, Henry,"
he said, "you have an awful lot of money
in that sock. You can get a lot of cookies
and candy with all that money."

"I could, couldn't I?" was all Henry said.

Chippy knew about the pennies.
But what he didn't know was that Henry had
put some peanuts in the sock, too.
The peanuts would be a present for Snowdrop.

When school was over for the day,
Henry ran out the door as fast as he could.
And Chippy ran right behind him.

When the boys got to the playground,
they saw balloons and tables.
There were people and food everywhere.
Chippy stopped for a hot dog and
some cookies. But Henry walked on.

123

"Want to ride a pony?" asked a girl
in a big hat.

"No, thanks," Henry said.
"Could you tell me where
the white elephant sale is?"

"I think it's at the other side
of the playground," said the girl.

Henry was scared that he would be
too late. He began to run. Then he saw
Chippy's mother behind a long table.
She saw Henry at the same time.

124

"How are you, Henry?" she asked.
"What can I do for you?"

"I'm here to buy it," said Henry.

"Buy what?" asked Chippy's mother.

"You know—the white elephant."

"Well," she said, "we have
a lot of things you can buy. Would you like
this soup spoon? You could give it
to your mother."

"I . . . . ." was all Henry said.

"Or this painted donkey? With a new tail,
it would look like new. Or how about
this red ball for your sister?"

"No," said Henry. "What I really want
is the little white elephant. I'm going
to call her Snowdrop. Where is she?"

"Henry," said Chippy's mother,
"we don't have any **real** elephants.
A white elephant is something someone has
and doesn't really want. That's what
all the things you see on the table are.
People who didn't want them gave them to us
for the White Elephant Sale. Other people
will buy them and take them home."

There was no live little white elephant?
Just some old things people didn't want?
Henry wanted to run away. He didn't want
Chippy's mother to see his tears.

Part Three
Snowdrop

Henry was about to leave
the White Elephant Sale. Then he saw
something move on another table.
The thing that moved was in a box
with holes. And it was white.

Henry walked over to see what it was.
There in the box was a very little rabbit!
It was white as snow. Henry put in his hand
to feel the rabbit. It was soft as could be.
It put its nose on Henry's hand.

Chippy's mother was watching. "She has a collar and leash," she said. "Why don't you play with her over there on the grass?"

Chippy's mother gave the collar and leash to Henry. He put them on the rabbit. Then he took the rabbit out of the box. "Come on," he said. And she came! She hopped, hopped, hopped along right behind Henry. He stopped. She stopped. Henry laughed. Then he looked at her.

"I think you want something to eat,"
he said. "Some grass, I bet." He thought
of the green grass in back of his house.
And he thought of the doghouse
that no one lived in.

Henry put his hand on her soft back.
He thought of how happy
this soft white rabbit would make
his baby sister. And to think no one wanted
this rabbit!

"Henry," called Chippy. "Wait for me.
Gee, where did you get that rabbit?"

Chippy's mother came up behind them.
"The fair will be over soon, boys," she said.
"Well, Henry, how do you like Snowdrop?"

"Snowdrop? How did you know her name?"
asked Henry.

"It's a very good name for a white rabbit,"
said Chippy's mother.

Slowly Henry asked, "How many pennies
for her? I have just three hundred."

"You can have her for two hundred pennies,"
she said. "And the collar and leash come
with her."

131

Henry counted out two hundred pennies
one by one. Just as he counted out the last
of the pennies, the peanuts fell out
of his sock. Henry cracked one open
and gave it to Snowdrop. She ate it up
and looked at Henry for more.

"She likes peanuts!" he said.
"When I get her home, she can eat grass
most of the time. But sometimes I'll give her
peanuts."

Henry put his hand in his sock.
He still had pennies to buy a balloon
for his baby sister and some cookies
for his mother and father.

Then all the pennies were gone.
Henry put his sock in his pocket.
He made sure he had all his things.

"Come on, Snowdrop," he said.
"Let's go home."

What Goes at the End?

Look at the special sign at the end of this sentence.

What a nice red car Carmen has!

This sentence shows surprise. It has an ! at the end.

Look at the special sign at the end of this sentence.

Have you seen Carmen's new car?

This sentence asks a question. It has a ? at the end.

Look at the special sign at the end of this sentence.

My brother has a car.

This sentence tells something. It has a . at the end.

Read each sentence below. The special
sign is missing from each sentence.
Write each sentence on your paper.
Use the right sign at the end of
each sentence.

1. May we go to the zoo today
2. How I like to go to the zoo
3. The zoo is on Lucky Street

4. The birthday present was on the table
5. What a great birthday present that is
6. Who gave me this birthday present

7. Debbie has a dog
8. Where is Debbie's dog
9. What a great big dog Debbie has

10. Harry eats breakfast every day
11. Did Harry eat breakfast yet
12. What a good breakfast

13. Look how well Winifred rides her bike
14. Can Winifred ride your bike
15. Winifred has a bike

BELIEVE IT

It's not as hard to learn something
new if you believe you can do things.
If you believe in what you can do,
you may find that you can do things
you never thought of doing.

Thinking About "Believe It!"

1. How did the little brown bear find out
   what job he could do best?
2. Why do you think other people didn't
   like the things Winifred made?
3. What kinds of things do people sometimes
   see when they look at clouds?
4. How did Henry find something special
   to buy with his pennies?
5. What kind of job do you think
   you could do best?

Glossary

A

a · bove   The bird flew <u>above</u> the house.

air   Music filled the <u>air</u>.

al · most   Betsy is <u>almost</u> seven years old.

an · gry   Rosa was <u>angry</u> because she got paint on her new dress.

a · sleep   Be very quiet and the baby will fall <u>asleep</u>.

B

bal · loons   I blew up two red <u>balloons</u> for the party.

bang   The door closed with a <u>bang</u>.

bark   My dog will <u>bark</u> when it wants to eat. Its <u>bark</u> is loud.

be · cause   I gave her a present <u>because</u> it is her birthday.

be · fore   The bird flew away <u>before</u> the cat could catch it.

be · hind   If we hide <u>behind</u> the tree, no one will see us.

blew   I <u>blew</u> up a balloon last night.

blow   Today I can <u>blow</u> up two balloons.

bot · tom   We ran down to the <u>bottom</u> of the hill.

bright   The sun was so <u>bright</u> that it hurt my eyes.

broth · er   My <u>brother</u> and I help our father clean the house.

buy   I will use my pennies to <u>buy</u> a red ball.

C

card   I made a birthday <u>card</u> for my grandmother.

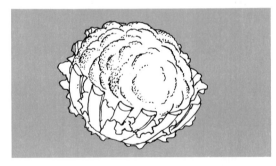

cau · li · flow · ers   Debbie grew <u>cauliflowers</u> last year.

cave   We found an old <u>cave</u> in the side of the mountain.

cir · rus   I saw small, white <u>cirrus</u> clouds in the sky this morning.

138

clouds   There were gray clouds in the sky before it rained.

col·lar   Sam put a collar on his dog.

col·lec·tors   Garbage collectors put all the garbage together and take it away.

cook·ies   I have milk and cookies when I get home from school

cu·mu·lus   I saw big, white cumulus clouds in the blue sky.

D

de·cid·ed   I decided to paint my bike red.

does·n't   The kitten doesn't want to stay in the box.

drag·on   The dragon in the story looks like a big lizard.

dry   The dry, brown grass needs rain.

E

ears   We use our ears to hear.

earth   You must dig up the earth before you can grow flowers.

el·e·phant   An elephant is a very strong animal.

e·ven   Even if it rains we will go to the park.

139

eve·ning   The sun goes down in the evening.

ev·er   This is the best doghouse I have ever seen.

eyes   We see with our eyes.

F

fair   I played a game and watched a clown at the fair.

feath·er·y   The white clouds looked soft and feathery.

Fri·day   Friday is the day after Thursday.

G

gi·ant   In the story, there was a giant dragon.

girls'   The girls' names are Kim and Sally.

H

hair   That girl has long, brown hair.

hard   Abe rode hard on his bike.

hard·ly   I was so late I hardly had time to eat breakfast.

hatch   The bird is ready to hatch from the egg.

hear   Can you hear the birds singing?

hel·lo   I say hello when I see my friends on the playground.

her·self   Ann can read this book all by herself.

high·est   This frog can jump the highest of them all.

hun·dred   I can count from one to one hundred.

I

I'd   I'd like to go to the park with you.

in·vis·i·ble   You cannot see things that are invisible.

J

job   Cleaning the house is a hard job.

K

knew   I wish I knew the answer.

L

lap When I sat down, the dog jumped into my lap.

laugh The funny clown made me laugh.

law The law says you must keep your dog on a leash.

lay The cat lay on the rug.

learn Fred will learn to read in school this year.

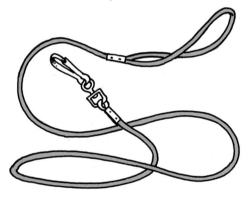

leash John put a leash on the dog to take it for a walk.

lick Cats lick their feet to keep them clean.

live Hal wants a real live rabbit for his birthday.

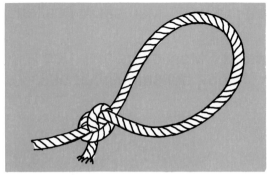

loop Larry made a loop at the end of the rope.

M

mad I got mad at my dog when it ran away.

main The main street is the most important street in a city.

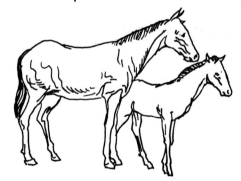

mares' Both mares' colts are brown.

mid·dle Don't ride your bike in the middle of the street.

missed Rico missed his friend who had moved away.

mis • ter A man can be called <u>mister</u>.

most <u>Most</u> of the time Joe is happy, but sometimes he is sad.

moun • tain The <u>mountain</u> is so high that clouds hide part of it.

Mr. <u>Mr.</u> Lopez is my teacher.

Mrs. <u>Mrs.</u> Potter is Ken's mother.

o • pen The <u>open</u> window let air in the room.

or • der The man next door gave me an <u>order</u> for two boxes of cookies.

pen • nies I can buy a balloon for six <u>pennies</u>.

pet My <u>pet</u> dog likes to play ball with me.

please <u>Please</u> help me push this door closed.

po • lice of • fi • cers The <u>police officers</u> found my dog when it ran away.

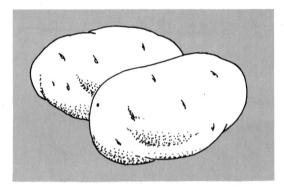

po • ta • toes <u>Potatoes</u> grow in the ground.

proud • ly Sandy pointed <u>proudly</u> to the picture he had painted.

puf • fy The rabbit has a <u>puffy</u>, white tail.

R

read • y It is time to leave, but I am not <u>ready</u> to go.

real • ly I cried when I cut my knee, because it <u>really</u> hurt.

riv·er   We can catch some fish in the river.

S

sale   There are kittens for sale at the pet shop.

scared   The dragon in the story scared me.

sev·en   I counted seven frogs in the lake.

show   I will show you how to ride your bike.

sky   Birds fly in the sky.

smal·ler   A kitten is smaller than a cat.

smart   Ben has a smart dog that can catch a ball.

spe·cial   Mother made a special breakfast on my birthday.

spoon   You eat soup with a spoon.

sto·ry   The best story is the one about the boy and the giant.

stra·tus   Stratus clouds are low and look like fog.

string   The kitten played with some string.

T

talk   Kate and Kim talk on the way to school.

tape   Put some tape on the box to keep it closed.

task   It is a hard task to rake leaves.

143

Thurs · days Thursdays are special days for Ben.

trav · el · ers The travelers waited for the boat to take them down the river.

trot Horses move fast when they trot.

trucks We needed two trucks to move our things to the new house.

turn It is my turn to ride the pony now.

W

wheel·chair People who can't walk use a wheelchair.

win · dow I closed the window to keep out the rain.

wings Birds use their wings to fly.

wish I have a fish, but I wish I had a dog.

won · der I wonder what I did with my crayons.

Y

yard My dog likes to play in our yard.

year I will be eight next year.

years Ann is seven years old today.

Z

zoo We gave peanuts to the elephants at the zoo.